Teddy's ABC

Brown Watson
ENGLAND

Text by Maureen Spurgeon
Illustrations by Pamela Storey

First Published 1993 by Brown Watson
The Old Mill, 76 Fleckney Road
Kibworth Beauchamp, Leics. England
© 1993 Brown Watson
Printed and bound in Belgium

"Come with me
And you shall see,
How to learn
Your **a b c**!
Meet my friends!
My family, too!
Each one of them
Will soon help you!
You'll find it's as easy
As it can be,
With us, to learn
Your **a b c**!"

Aa

"Here I am, at my school –
We have lessons every day.
Is there something on my desk
Which begins with a letter **a**?
That's right! It's an **a**pple!
But, that isn't all –
Just look at the posters
Teacher's put on the wall!
There's an **a**nt, **a**lligator –
And an **a**rk, by the way . . .
An **a**crobat . . . what else
Begins with an **a**?"

Bb

"Lots of things here
Which begin with a **b**!
Barney **B**ear in his **b**oots –
And then – there is ME!
B is for **b**ear,
Birds and a **b**all,
A **b**us and a **b**icycle –
Now, is that all?
There are **b**elts on our coats
So, just look and see
How many more things
Begin with a **b**!"

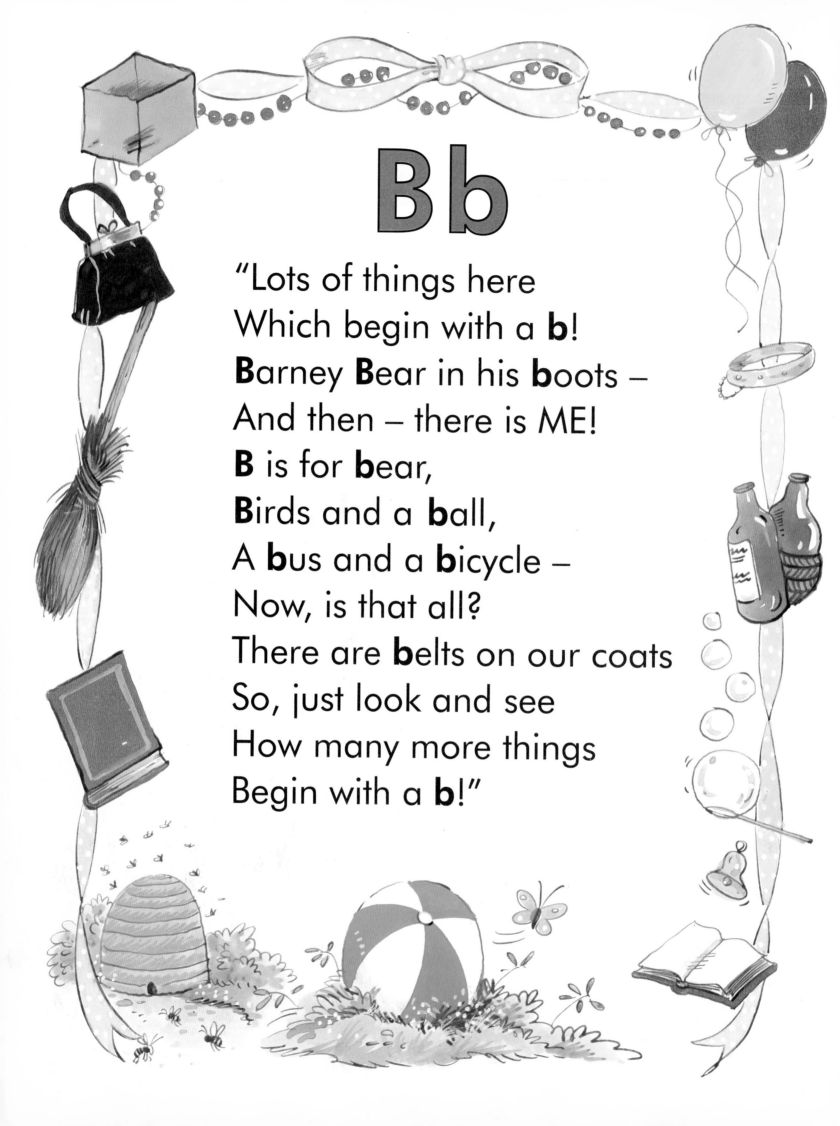

Cc

"Picnic time, now!
And the next letter's **c**.
There are **c**ups for our drinks
And our **c**at – can you see?
We eat **c**arrots and **c**ake
And ripe **ch**erries, too!
And **ch**ocolate! Delicious!
Now, let me tell you –
Ch may be
Rather different a sound –
But the first letter's **c**.
Any more to be found?"

Dd

"Our next letter's **d**,
Which starts my **d**og's name –
He's **D**anny, the **d**og,
And he just loves a game!
Then there's **D**aisy the **d**onkey,
Another good friend.
She'll never bite
Or try to offend!
See **d**uck and the **d**ucklings,
And a big **d**ragonfly –
Any more letter **d** words?
Play a game of I-Spy!"

Ee Ff Gg Hh

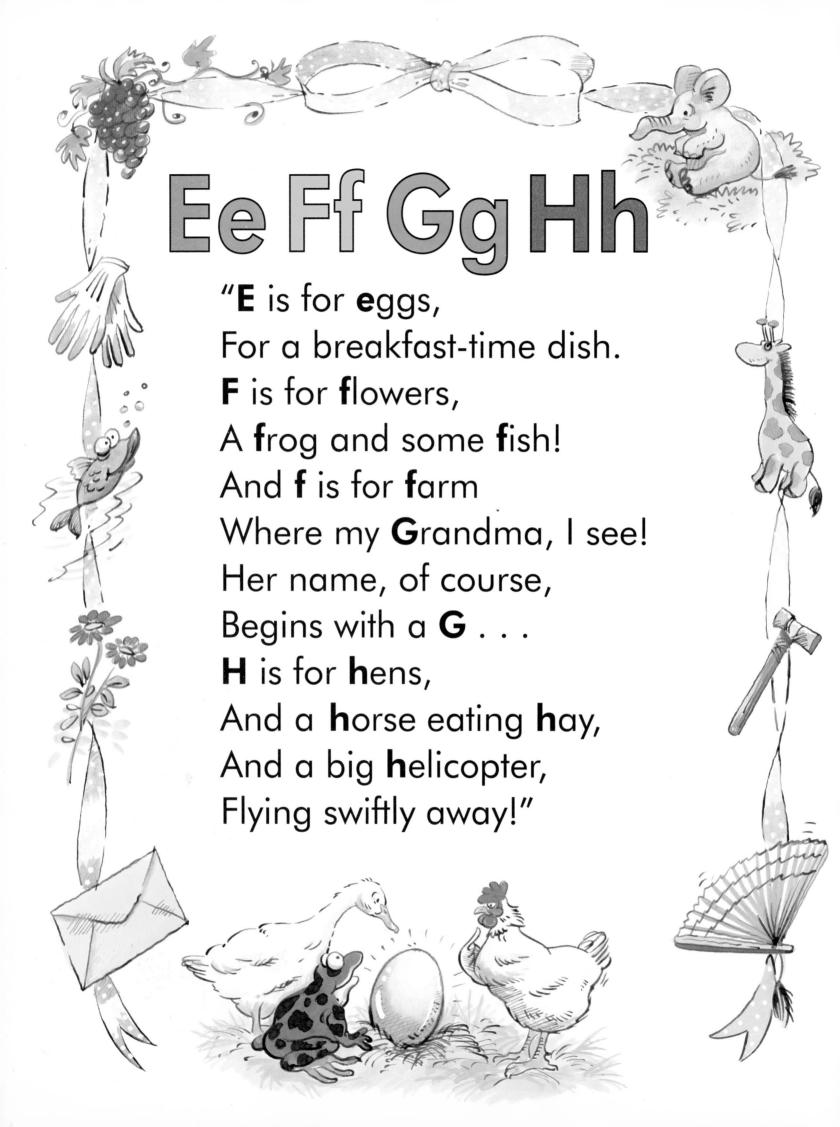

"**E** is for **e**ggs,
For a breakfast-time dish.
F is for **f**lowers,
A **f**rog and some **f**ish!
And **f** is for **f**arm
Where my **G**randma, I see!
Her name, of course,
Begins with a **G** . . .
H is for **h**ens,
And a **h**orse eating **h**ay,
And a big **h**elicopter,
Flying swiftly away!"

Ii Jj Kk

"**I** is for **i**ce-cream –
My favourite treat!
Jack-in-the-Box
Would love some to eat!
His name, you know,
Begins with a **J** –
And a big **j**ug of **j**uice
Begins the same way!
Then there's **k** for **k**oala,
My **k**ite and a **k**ing,
And a **k**itten which makes
Knots in the **k**nitting!"

Ll

"**L** is for **l**aces –
One of mine is undone!
A strong **l**ead for Danny –
Every dog should have one.
There are **l**eaves on the trees
And **l**ettuce for tea,
A bright **l**adybird, and
A **l**ollipop for me!
Then a **l**adder for Daddy,
And some **l**etters, too,
Brought by the postman –
Any more words for you?"

Mm

"**M** is for **m**edicine
To take when we're ill –
The **m**oon through my window –
So bright and so still . . .
Then, **m** for the **m**ilk
Which **M**ummy brings me.
And I know there's a **m**ouse –
Take a look! Can you see?
Money and **m**oneybox,
Mushrooms – see them?
How many more things
Begin with an **m**?"

Nn Oo Pp

"Now we are out camping!
Can you see a **n**est!
A **n**ewspaper for Daddy –
That's what he likes best.
Nest and **n**ewspaper
Both begin with an **n** –
There are **n**uts and a **n**et,
What's the next letter, then?
It's **o** for an **o**wl!
And next comes a **p**,
Which begins **p**ath and **p**illows –
Any more? Look and see!"

Qq Rr Ss

"The next letter is **q**
Which begins the word **q**ueen –
Though, here in our park,
There's not one to be seen!
The **r**ain and the **r**abbits
Begin with – can you guess?
That's right! It's an **r**!
And the next letter's **s**
We have **s** for **s**ee-**s**aw,
A **s**lide and some **s**wings!
Look hard! You may notice
Quite a few other things!"

Tt Uu

"Now, the next letter
Is special to me.
Can you think just why?
It is letter **t**!
Yes! **T** for **T**eddy –
Television, too!
The **t**rack and a **t**unnel . . .
Now, the next letter's **u**
Which begins **u**mbrella
To help keep us dry,
When rain begins falling
From clouds in the sky."

Vv Ww

"**V** for the **v**iolin
Which my Daddy plays.
He's a fine **v**iolinist
Doing practice most days.
There's **v**olcano and **v**ase –
Both begin with a **v** –
W comes next –
Through the **w**indow, you'll see
The **w**ell, with the **w**ater
Which is for us all.
Then Daddy's **w**heelbarrow,
Which he's left by the **w**all!"

Xx Yy Zz

"Now, **x** for the **x**ylophone
I'd like to play!
I had one, you see,
For my birthday, today!
Letter **x** often ends words –
Like si**x**, fi**x** and fo**x** . . .
Then, **y** for my **y**acht –
It was packed in a bo**x**!
Tomorrow, I'm taking it
Out for a sail!
Then **z** is for **z**ebra,
With stripes to his tail!"

Aa

Bb

Cc

Dd

Ee

Ff

Gg

Hh

Ii

Jj

Kk

Ll

Mm

Nn

Oo

Pp

Qq

Rr

Ss

Tt

Uu

Vv

Ww

Xx

Yy

Zz

"Time to go!
But, now you see
How you can learn
Your **a b c**!
And if you'd like
Our help again,
Just turn the pages,
Look – and then,
You'll find it easy
As can be,
To learn, with us,
Your **a b c**!"